THE ⌐ OF DAYS

THE
DARKEST
OF DAYS

Senghennydd disaster, 1913

Gareth F. Williams

Images by Graham Howells

Gwasg Carreg Gwalch

First published in Welsh: 2014
English translation:
© text: Gareth F. Williams 2016
© images: Graham Howells 2014

ISBN: 978-1-84527-493-1

Published with the financial support
of the Welsh Books Council

Published by Gwasg Carreg Gwalch,
12 Iard yr Orsaf, Llanrwst, Dyffryn Conwy, Cymru LL26 0EH.
tel: 01492 642031
fax: 01492 642502
email: books@carreg-gwalch.com
website: www.carreg-gwalch.com

In memory of all lost at Senghennydd,

1901 a 1913

'It was a little after eight on Tuesday morning
when a dreadful sound was heard . . .'

A ballad of the disaster

The Allotment

14 October 1963

John Williams straightened up in his chair.

'I'm just popping down to the allotment,' he announced.

'So I see.' His wife, Betty, had been watching him as he struggled to jam his feet inside his wellingtons. She smiled. The council allotments had been a godsend for John since he'd retired.

'The forecast was for rain, mind,' Betty warned him.

'Pah!' John pulled on his coat.

And what, pray tell, did *that* mean? Betty wondered. Was it, 'Pah! A spot of rain never did me any harm!', or, 'Pah! You can't believe a single word those so-called weather forecasters say!'?

But instead of asking him what he meant, Betty said, 'John, are you feeling all right?'

'What? Yes, of course I am. Why?' John answered tetchily.

'You've been ... well, a bit quiet these last few days,' Betty said. 'And when you're not quiet, you're snapping at me. What's the matter?'

Before John could reply, a voice called from the front door: 'Anyone home?'

John sighed impatiently.

'In here!' Betty called back, before turning to her husband with a frown. 'What on earth is wrong with you, man? It's *Rhian* – your daughter!'

'I know that.'

Rhian came through to the kitchen, and John and Betty were surprised to see that Geraint, her ten-year-old son, was with her.

'And what's this?' exclaimed Betty. 'Don't tell me those teachers are on strike again.'

'I wish that was all,' Rhian said. 'We've just been to the dentist. *Someone* kept us all awake last night with a nasty toothache.'

'A toothache?'

John Williams was staring at the poor boy as though Geraint had said he'd contracted some rare tropical disease.

'You had a toothache – *today*?'

'Last night was the worst of it, Dad,' said Rhian, looking at him strangely. Why had he reacted like this to Geraint's news?

'It's gone now, Taid,' said Geraint, 'along with the tooth.'

He removed a bloody piece of tissue from his pocket and unfolded it. There lay the tooth, looking a bit forlorn.

Normally, John Williams would have made a big fuss over something like this. But not this time. All he did today was shake his head a couple of times before turning for the door.

'I'll be back by lunch-time,' he muttered over his shoulder.

'Oh – before you disappear,' said Rhian, 'are you coming round tonight, or what?'

'Eh?'

'There's a programme on the telly you might enjoy.' John and Betty didn't own a television set, only a huge old brown wireless that dominated one corner of the living room. 'About Senghennydd. It's fifty years since the disaster happened, Dad. *Remembering Senghennydd* – that's what it's called. It's on at half-past seven ...'

Rhian's words trailed off. Her father was glaring at her as though she'd just spat in his face.

'Why the hell would I want to watch something like that?' he snarled. And out he went, slamming the door behind him.

An hour later, John sat inside his little shed looking out at the rain sweeping across the allotment. Betty was spot-on, he thought ruefully – her and those weather-prophets on the wireless.

'But as for *you*, John Williams,' he said to himself, 'your behaviour was a long way from being spot-on. And Geraint, the poor little mite, having just had his tooth yanked out and all.'

It was one heck of a coincidence, though – odd, if not downright eerie: that Geraint had suffered from a raging toothache *today*, of all days.

Because precisely the same thing had happened to John Williams's father.

Fifty years ago, to the day.

In Senghennydd.

John sighed heavily. '*You've been a bit quiet these last few days*' – those were Betty's words, weren't they? '*And when you're not quiet, you're snapping at me.*' Dead right, Betty, as always. John wasn't a taciturn man by nature, and he liked to think he was far from being a grumpy old meanie. But today had been weighing heavily on his mind for some weeks now.

Remembering Senghennydd, indeed. He didn't need some blasted television programme to help him remember Senghennydd, ta very much. Not a day went by when he *didn't* think about Senghennydd – even though almost fifty years had gone by since he'd said goodbye to the place.

Hadn't John Williams lost both his father and his best friend there?

Now, as he listened to the rain pounding onto the roof of his cosy little shed in the allotments, his mind wandered back over the years ... to Senghennydd.

Part 1

ALL RIGHT, BUTTY?

The Letter

1908

Kate Williams, John's mother, sat as still as a statue with the letter open on the table in front of her.

She'd read it, John knew. Several times, if he knew his mother. But she wasn't even looking at it now. Her mind was somewhere else – somewhere far, far away.

And her eyes were shining with an awful wetness.

This is how John knew that this was *the* letter. Yet, he still had to ask.

'Mam ...?' he ventured. 'Has ... has my dad's letter come at last?'

John glanced down at the ... the *thing* ... lying there on the table, two pages filled with his father's familiar scrawl. He felt a sudden urge to to snatch the letter off the table and tear it into tiny slivers, before dropping each individual piece into the kitchen fire.

But of course, that wouldn't change anything.

'Is that it, Mam?' he asked.

Kate Williams nodded slowly without looking at her son.

'Yes, John, this is it,' she said. 'Come at last ...'

She burst into tears.

The three-year-long strike at the local slate quarry had had a devastating effect on the district. With hardly any money coming into the house, Edward Williams – John's father – had, along with several other local men, been forced to seek work elsewhere.

He'd heard that there were plenty of jobs going at the coal mines down in south Wales. One warm, sunny spring morning, off he went on the train.

'As soon as I get settled properly, I'll send for you to join me,' he said to Kate, John and Magwen. 'It won't take me long, you'll see. One day soon, you too will be sitting on this train, travelling all the way down south.'

And now, according to the spidery words that crawled across those two sheets of paper on the kitchen table, that day was about to dawn.

'When are you off, then?' asked Ned.

The two boys were sitting on the mountainside, gazing down over the village.

'I don't know, exactly,' John replied. 'Pretty soon. We'll be there before we know it, Mam says.'

'Really?'

Ned gaped at him. He was obviously finding it difficult to imagine this.

'Before you know it?' he marvelled. 'Whatever next?'

John just had to look away – his eyes had suddenly filled with hot tears. I'll miss old Ned, he thought, miss him terribly. Good old Whatever Next Ned, as everyone called him, as he only had to hear of the least thing that was out of the ordinary for him to marvel and say, 'Whatever next?'

'I'd always thought the south was quite far away,' he said.

'Well – yes, it is,' agreed John.

'Oh ...? But you've just said that you'll be there before you know it.'

'I know. But some things have a way of happening very quickly,' replied John.

Particularly things I don't want to happen, he thought. They always – always – happen at great speed. But he wasn't going to mention that to Ned, not when he was trying his best to be brave about it all.

But Ned seemed to have read his mind.

'Are you looking forward to going down south?' he asked.

''Course I am!' John answered – a little too quickly. 'I can't wait, Ned.'

'Can't you?'

'No, I can't. Honestly.'

'I see,' said Ned.

The two boys were quiet for a few minutes. When, at last, Ned spoke, his voice shook in a funny way.

'I can't wait either,' he said.

'What ...?' said John. 'What d'you mean?'

'I can't wait for you to go,' said Ned. He sprang to his feet and ran away down the mountain path, as fast as his feet could carry him.

'Ned!' John yelled after him. 'Ned – wait!'

But Whatever Next Ned had gone.

John saw very little of his friend over the next few weeks. Moving away, he was surprised to discover, involved *a lot* of hard work and he was kept busy from the moment he got up until he was finally allowed to collapse back into bed. Matters weren't helped by his little sister, Magwen, who'd been transformed into a bundle of excitement and seemed to delight in getting under his feet at every opportunity. 'At least one of us is looking forward to moving down south,' John overheard his mother remark to Lizzie Hughes, their next door neighbour, one day.

And as his mother had warned him, Departure Day was upon him almost before he knew it. Many of their friends and neighbours had accompanied them to the railway station to say goodbye, but try as he might, John couldn't spot Ned's face among them.

But as the train began to jerk slowly out of the station, there was Ned, standing in the shade of one of the tall trucks parked in a siding. The two boys stared at each other, then Ned started to raise his arm in a wave before letting it drop limply back down to his side, as though his arm had suddenly become too heavy for him to raise it any higher.

Then he turned and walked back towards home.

Home, thought John. Home ...

One little word, but it was big enough to fill his eyes with tears.

'Enough of that childish nonsense, John Williams,' he chided himself. 'You must be positive, for Mam's sake, and for Magwen's. I've got a new Home now,' he repeated to himself, over and over.

A new home .... a new home ... a new home ...

A New Home

'The Tower of Babel,' was Kate Williams's frequent remark during those first few weeks. 'That's what this place is like – the Tower of Babel.'

John had heard about this Tower of Babel at Sunday school, when he was still living at 'Old Home'. It was mentioned in the Bible, a tall tower filled with people jabbering away in different languages.

'Did they use to speak Welsh there as well?' he remembered asking Daniel Ellis, his Sunday school teacher.

Mr Ellis had stroked his moustache, something he always did whenever someone asked him a difficult question.

'I'm certain they must have done, John,' he answered at last. 'Welsh of some kind, at any rate.'

During his first weeks in Senghennydd, John often thought about Mr Ellis's words. But he soon came to realise that the people he heard on the streets only *sounded* as though they were talking in a foreign language. It was just that their accent was so different to his own. The only other language he heard was English, hardly a strange, new tongue for him. Bit by bit, he came to recognise and tell the difference between Irish accents and Scottish accents, as well as those of people who'd come here from different parts of England in search of work – from Cornwall and Somerset, from London and from Liverpool and the north of England.

And people from different parts of Wales too, of course.

Although, to begin with, there had been a tiny problem.

'Can you understand them when they talk to you, Dad?' he asked.

'Aye, butty-boy!' answered his father.

'*What?*'

Edward Williams laughed. John's father was a tall man, with straight black hair and a moustache that grew down past the sides of his mouth.

'Yes, on the whole, old mate,' he translated. 'So will you, before very long, you'll see. Far too much fuss is made of this we-can't-understand-one-another nonsense. We're all Welsh, aren't we? It's only a matter of getting used to each other's accents, that's all.'

The New Home – the house itself – wasn't all that different from John's Old Home. This one, too, was one in a row of terraced houses, with two upstairs bedrooms, a front parlour, a kitchen and a smaller kitchen – or scullery – on the ground floor.

But the funny thing was ...

Back at John's Old Home, his parents used to pay the rent to a man called W. J. Parry. Here, the rent for the New Home went to a man called W. J. Paris. He was a pink-faced, small man, but filled with self-importance, never seen without a suit and a bowler hat and who insisted that the correct way of pronouncing his name was 'Pareeee' – and instead of rolling the 'r', he'd say it as though there was a huge glob of phlegm rattling around inside his throat.

'That's how French people pronounce Paris,' said Edward Williams, 'or so I'm told.'

'Huh. He's nothing but a pompous old fool,' was Kate's opinion of Mr W. J. Pareeee. 'He thinks he's better than anyone else.'

'Oh, I know – but we don't want to start off on the wrong foot by offending the rent-man, do we?' said Edward. He shook his head, smiling. 'Who'd have thought it, eh? W. J. Parry and W. J. Pareeee. It's almost like being back home, isn't it, Kate?'

Kate said nothing.

'And once all your furniture has been delivered here from the station – especially your gran's old dresser – you'll feel so much better,' Edward went on, giving her hair a playful tug.

Kate had nodded and tried to smile, but it was a weak and crooked little smile; John noticed too that his mother's eyes had that upsetting, wet shine to them once again.

He turned to his little sister.

'Come on,' he said. 'Let's go out the back and have a proper look round.'

Stepping out into the back yard, the first thing John and Magwen saw was a huge tin bath hanging precariously from two nails that had been hammered into the high wall that separated their house from next door's.

'Well then, Maggie, what d'you think of this place, so far?' John asked.

For once, Magwen didn't scold him for calling her Maggie. He noticed that she looked a little pale, tired out after her long journey down here as well as from the excitement of moving house.

'I want to go home.' Her lower lip quivered as she spoke.

So do I, thought John. But he'd never have admitted this to his little sister.

He said instead, 'This is our home now.'

'Never!' Maggie insisted. She turned a complete circle, looking upwards and taking in all four points of the compass. 'Where's the mountain, then?'

She was right, too. Come to think of it, John realised, there wasn't a *proper* mountain anywhere near the place.

'It's not *Home*, then, is it?' Magwen went on, and gave a resounding wallop to the tin bath hanging off the wall.

Exactly as if she'd rung a bell to summon them, six heads suddenly popped up on the other side of the wall – one after the other and all in a row. No actual bodies were to be seen at all – only the six heads – and Magwen leapt backwards in fright.

These heads, thought John, look as if some cruel king had separated them from the bodies with a huge axe, and had then propped them up on top of the wall as a warning to the people of his kingdom: this is what'll happen to you if you don't behave yourselves.

(Neither John nor Magwen knew this yet, of course, but the six heads belonged to the Dando children – Billy, Blodwen, Sean, Jane, Jemima and Little Jo.)

'All right, butty?' said the first head (Billy's).

'What did he say?' Magwen whispered between her teeth, managing somehow to do so without moving her lips.

'Er ... he's asking if his sandwich is all right ... I think,' John whispered back.

'How does he expect *us* to know that? Magwen asked.

'*I* don't know, do I!' John whispered. He raised his voice. 'Er ... sorry ... I don't know ... ' he said to the head.

The first head swivelled to the left and looked down along the row at the other five heads.

The other five heads swivelled to the right and stared back at the first head.

But before any of them could utter anything further, a woman's voice shattered the silence with a loud 'HOY!' One by one, the six heads vanished from atop the wall, as if someone had walked along the other side plucking their owners down by their feet.

John and Magwen looked at each other.

'Something tells me,' said John, 'that our dad has brought us to a very strange part of the country. What d'you think, Maggie ...? Ouch!'

'Don't call me Maggie!'

Magwen ran back into the house. John smiled. *Someone* is beginning to feel better already, he said to himself.

That just leaves Mam and me.

The Pit

Universal Colliery – that's what the pit was called.

The coal mine ...

Unfortunately, John couldn't help but think of Whatever Next Ned whenever he said or heard – or even *thought* of – the word 'miner'.

And of course, whenever he thought of Ned, he thought of his Old Home, and a terrible feeling of *hiraeth* would stab him in the pit of his stomach, almost as if someone had plunged one of his Mam's knitting needles through his belly button.

Coal mine ... miner ... poor old Ned. He hadn't had a clue what a miner was. When John first told him that his dad was thinking of going down south to work as a miner, Ned had gaped at him.

'Your *dad*?' he'd said.

'Well – yes,' John replied.

'Is that *all* he's going to be?'

'That's what he told me,' said the bemused John. 'Why, what's the matter with that? There's very little work to be had in the quarries these days, is there? And money doesn't grow on trees, you know,' he added. He'd heard his father use this expression and had taken a liking to it.

Ned sneered. 'He won't get paid much, if he's only going to be a miner.'

John bristled. 'Dad says the miners getter better wages than the quarrymen do. He'll be paid a lot more than your dad gets.'

Another sneer. 'Not if he's only going to be a miner.'

John felt totally lost. What the heck was Ned blathering about? And since when had he become such an expert on coal miners' wages, anyway?

Then Ned said, '*My* dad would never go all that way just to be a miner. They'd have to make him a Major, at least.'

He'd nodded seriously and John had struggled not to laugh. But poor Ned's confusion had caused much merriment when John got home that day, and Edward Williams had repeated a joke told to him by one of his friends.

'What musical note would you hear if a piano fell down a mine shaft?'

John had shaken his head. 'Don't know ...'

'A flat miner! Get it? A-flat minor ...'

'Yes, all right, Edward,' Kate had snapped.

'Hey, come on, it's only a joke,' Edward said.

'It isn't a very funny one. Not at all funny, in fact. People get killed in those mines.'

'They get killed in the quarries too ...' Edward Williams sighed. 'Kate, love – I'm doing my best ...'

John's mother had nodded, tight-lipped, and the rest of that night's supper had been finished in silence.

Later, when John stepped into the back kitchen to say good night, his mother was standing there in the middle of the floor, looking lost, as if she'd fallen asleep in her own home and woken up in someone else's.

And when she turned to look at John, it was as if she barely recognised him.

Months later, in their new home, it was John who barely recognised his own father the first time he saw Edward Williams arrive home at the end of his shift. He was covered in coal dust, and so black that John had to peer at him before realising who he was – and that was only when his father greeted him with his usual 'How are things, 'ngwas i?'

Poor Magwen hadn't recognised her father at all. She was sitting at the table and drawing on a piece of paper when Edward strode into the room. Glancing up, she saw this huge black face with two white circles around its eyes looking down at her. She let out a loud yell of terror before leaping to her feet and galloping up the stairs, screaming her head off.

'Good grief, girl, anyone would think you were being murdered!' Kate exclaimed. 'It's only your dad.'

But Magwen was cowering under her parents' bed by then,

and she refused to come back out until Edward Williams had washed all the coal dust from his face.

After washing (and lying on the floor to show Magwen – who was still hiding under the bed – his clean face) and having a bite to eat, Edward said to John, 'Come on – let's you and I go for a little walk.'

'Where?' John asked.

'Just around the village, so you can get to know your new home. We shan't be long, Kate.'

He kissed Kate's cheek and the top of Magwen's head, and he and John left the house. Once they were outside, John remembered something he'd been meaning to ask his father.

'Dad, what's a butty?'

'What? Oh – *butty*. Well, by now it means a friend, a mate,' Edward replied. 'But I think it originally meant someone who worked with you down in the same section of the pit.'

'Ah ... right.'

John was thinking about the six heads that had appeared on top of next door's back yard wall, and how the first head had muttered something about a 'butty'.

'It's got nothing to do with a sandwich, then?'

'A sandwich?' Edward frowned, then his face cleared and he burst out laughing. 'Ah, I see. Well, you're not that far off target, as it happens. The word *butty* has derived from the English slang word for a sandwich, because the miners all stop work and eat their sandwiches together at lunch-time – eating their butties with their butties, if you like. Mind you, you don't need to be close friends with someone to call him a butty. It's become a form of greeting by now. Just as we say, "How's things, pal?", they say …'

'All right, butty …' John finished, remembering what the owner of the first head had said to him. He felt a bit of a fool now – 'a bit of a donkey', as Kate often said. The boy next door had only been trying to be friendly. He probably thinks I'm a right snob, or that there's something wrong with me, John thought ruefully.

As it was a warm and sunny summer's evening, the people of Senghennydd were out on the streets enjoying the sun before it slipped out of sight behind the hills to the west. John heard several people greet his father with the by now familiar 'All right, butt?', as he and John walked down towards the colliery.

But it wasn't long before John stopped noticing, because

by then all his thoughts were taken over by the colliery itself. It was huge!

He'd never been this close to it before now. He'd seen the tall black chimney, of course, but hadn't quite realised just how high it reached. He gaped at the thick cloud of black smoke that was belching from its mouth, and as the sun had begun to set, the smoke looked like it was being sucked into a huge fire, ablaze with orange-red flames.

'Hell!' John exclaimed without thinking, then, remembering who he was with, cast an anxious glance at his father.

But Edward Williams was laughing. 'That's exactly what I said when I saw it properly for the first time.'

They stood there for a long while gazing at the colliery. John's eyes danced from the tall chimney to the huge, strong pithead wheels; wandered over the huts and all the different sheds – each one of those also with thick smoke curling out of its roof – and over the trucks standing on a small railway track, some of them empty but others piled high with coal, waiting to be shunted off to who knew where.

'All over the world,' his father told him later. 'The coal from south-east Wales is the best type, you see, and there's a huge demand for it world-wide.'

The coal seemed to be sweating blood in the red glow of the sunset. Edward Williams cleared his throat.

'There was a terrible accident here a little over three years ago,' he said. 'May 1901 – that's when it happened. Eighty-two men were killed here.'

'*How many*?' John said in astonishment. 'All at the same time?'

Edward nodded. 'An explosion. It must have been awful. I'm just grateful I wasn't here to see it.'

Eighty-two – in just one accident. Of course, fatal accidents were far from uncommon in the slate quarries back home, but more often than not they tended to happen to individual workers. John found it difficult to imagine eighty-two men dying at the same time.

'Will I be working here one day' he asked his father, 'with you and Mr Morgan?'

Moc Morgan was Edward's partner in the pit. Although they worked in the same section, they seldom worked *together*, as Edward would work one shift and Moc the other: one doing the day shift and the other taking on the night shift. If anything, Edward saw more of Moc Morgan at the chapel than he did down the pit.

Edward hesitated before answering John. Had John looked up in time, he'd have seen his father jerk his gaze away from the colliery as though he hated to even look at it.

'Perhaps ... ' he said finally. 'We'll wait and see, John, all right? Come on – we'd better start making tracks for home.'

The Huts

They set off along a street of small, impoverished-looking houses that lay in the shadow of the colliery.

'This street is known as the Huts,' said Edward. 'I suppose it's because the houses are little better than sheds.'

John noticed that several of the men seated on chairs outside their open front doors had their eyes closed and their faces turned up towards the sun.

'You'd be like that too, John, had you spent the entire day in the darkness of the pit,' Edward remarked. 'The winter's the worst. It's dark when you get up and set off for work, you spend the day underground in pitch darkness, and by the time you've completed your shift and come back up to the surface, it's dark again.' A sad expression took over his face as he gazed in the direction of the distant hills. 'That's what I miss most about the quarry,' he said. 'Sometimes, I feel like I'd happily give away a month's wages, just to spend one day out in the open air. Even if it's pouring with rain ... hey, stop that staring, boy! Come on ... '

John's attention had been seized by a collier who sat on a small wooden stool outside one of the houses. He had a tin bucket on his lap, into which he'd cough and spit in the most terrible fashion. John had never heard such an awful, racking cough in his life. It sounded to him as if the poor man's insides were being torn apart like some old cloth, and as John stared at him, dark red spittle flowed from the collier's mouth and into the bucket.

'What's wrong with him, Dad?' John asked as they hurried away from the man.

'Coal dust, 'ngwas i. Damn and drat the wretched thing! Heaven knows, slate dust in the quarries was bad enough, but *this* stuff ...'

That's when John felt a sharp blow on his back. Someone had thrown a stone at him. He turned to see a crowd of children staring boldly after them.

'What's up, John?' Edward asked.

'Nothing.'

John turned away from the children and carried on walking. Then he felt another stone hitting him – and yet another one a moment later: the first one striking him painfully between his shoulder blades and the second one hitting his calf and causing him to stumble.

'Good lord, what's wrong with you, boy? Are you drunk or something?' laughed Edward, but his grin vanished as another stone bounced along the ground between them.

'What the devil ... ?'

Edward turned and saw the children behind them. There were five of them in all, and when they saw Edward stop and turn, four of them turned and fled, speeding off in different directions like fish in a stream when someone's shadow falls over them.

One boy, however, stood his ground. He was around the same age as John, perhaps a year older, with reddish-brown hair that looked as if it had rusted. Looking at him, John was immediately reminded of a rat; the boy had a thin, pale and pointed face and his two front teeth were much larger and longer than the others. He displayed these yellow fangs now as he grinned cheekily at Edward Williams, as if he was challenging him to do something.

'Hey!' Edward said.

'Hey!' the boy echoed, raising his chin defiantly in John and Edward's direction.

'Who threw those stones? Was it you, lad?' Edward asked.

Perhaps Edward's north Walian accent had made it difficult for the boy to have understood every single word, but he'd understood enough for him to make a huge pantomime of looking around him and in every direction, before looking back at Edward and raising his shoulders, the picture of innocence. Edward glared at him for a few moments, but the boy just stood there, glaring back at Edward as though mimicking him.

Eventually, Edward said, 'Come on, before I lose my rag and end up doing something terrible to that cheeky little monkey.'

They'd only just begun to walk away when yet another stone shot towards them like a bullet, this time striking John in the head. He yelled with pain and turned to see his father striding towards the boy, who stood there watching his approach with a spiteful half-smile, making his features look even more rat-like.

In his hand was another stone, ready to be hurled, but before he had a chance to do so Edward Williams had grabbed him by the wrist. Now it was the boy's turn to yell in pain as the stone fell to the ground.

'What the devil d'you think you're playing at, boy?' Edward roared at him.

A moment later, and he was hopping on his left foot as the boy had delivered a vicious kick to his right leg. Edward released the boy, who turned and darted off into the dark doorway of one of the houses – just like a rat vanishing into a hole in a wall, thought John.

Edward Williams stood in the street, rubbing his leg. 'Unbelievable!' he kept muttering, more to himself than to John. 'I've never seen such a vicious little ... '

But there was worse to come.

They both turned as a loud bellowing – rather like that made by a bull in pain – exploded from the interior of the boy's house. Could a human throat be responsible for such a sound? Although the door was wide open, an ominous, almost solid darkness seemed to fill the doorway, making it resemble some dark and hideous cave that housed an even darker and more hideous beast.

Then a woman came out of the house. A *huge* woman. John had never before seen a woman as massive as this one. Because she was so large and because the doorway was so narrow, she emerged through it like one of those ships in a bottle squeezing its way out through the bottle's neck. John could have sworn that the earth trembled and shook as she lumbered across the street to where he and Edward stood gaping.

Like the stone-throwing boy, she too had rusty-looking hair, except that hers was slightly more orange in shade, very crinkly and shooting out in all directions. Her arms were fat and white like the large pieces of dough that Idw Hughes the Baker used to pummel on a wooden table back at John's Old Home. To crown it all she had a pipe jutting from her mouth, and she now jerked it out, spat on the ground and commenced haranguing Edward.

'You! You leave me boy alone!' she thundered.

'What?' said the incredulous Edward. 'Good God, *he* was the one who was throwing ... '

'You 'eard me, you ********!'

And from this terrible woman's mouth flowed a tidal wave of curses and all the swear words John had ever heard, as well as many he'd never heard before. Neither he nor his father had ever heard such foul language issuing from anyone's mouth. Several of the quarrymen back home were fluent swearers – *Duw mawr*, yes! Many of them were unable to communicate at all unless they were swearing like troopers, but even they failed to come anywhere close to the standard set by this woman.

She finished by saying, ' ... and I'll get me 'usband and 'is mates to sort you out!'

Husband? thought John. Good grief, what sort of man would choose to be married to monster like this? Did such a creature even exist?

One did, indeed, and it transpired that he'd been there all the time, standing in the shade behind his wife. Now he came into sight, bit by bit, as if he was sniffing the air. If the boy had resembled a rat, then his father was the spitting image of one. Exactly like a rat emerging from behind a large haystack, John thought.

He was nowhere near as tall as Edward Williams, but he had a mean, spiteful face. Like his son, he too had two large yellow front teeth, and he bared them now as he snarled at Edward.

'You heard the missus, pal,' he said, poking Edward in the chest with a bony finger. 'Nobody messes with my lad, all right? Nobody.' Another poke with his finger. 'I haven't finished with you yet, Northman,' he said. 'Not by a long chalk.'

The two of them turned and marched off, back to their

house, leaving Edward to gape after them, open-mouthed. John half-expected to see that the man had a long whip-like tail as he entered the house first, leaving his wife to squeeze her way inside after him.

'Good God ... ' said Edward Williams, looking like a man who'd just woken up from some awful nightmare. 'Good God ... '

As they once again set off for home, John noticed something

that had previously escaped him. Although there were many people out on the street, no one had taken a blind bit of notice of the little drama that had just been played out right under their noses. No one had even glanced in their direction, let alone come to their aid.

Something like this would never have happened back home, reflected John. Had a child been throwing stones like that little rat-boy had done, then a chorus of adult voices would have yelled at him or her to stop it at once; had he or she carried on regardless, then someone would have given him or her a good clout.

And as for challenging and kicking a grown-up like Edward Williams, well, he'd have been marched home to face a sound thrashing from his parents. More than likely, too, the parents would have called at Edward's house, full of apologies. They certainly wouldn't have cursed him and called him every foul name under the sun, or threatened him the way the bigger rat had done.

'Thank heaven we don't have to live next door to rubbish like that,' said Edward as they turned into their street. 'The best thing to do from now on, 'ngwas i, is to keep well away from them.'

But John had a nasty feeling that things weren't going to be that simple.

The Dandos

Approaching the house, they saw that the front door was wide open. But this wasn't what caused them both to stop abruptly and look at each other in amazement – after all, most of their neighbours' doors were wide open, too, on such a pleasant evening.

What, then?

The unexpected and unusual sound that could be heard coming from their house, that's what. A sound that neither John nor his father had heard for quite a while. For months. Since before Edward Williams announced that he was leaving for the south to look for work.

It was the sound of Kate laughing.

'Is that *Mam*?' John asked.

Edward Williams grinned happily. 'Yes, John – your mam!'

They hurried for the house, which was full of people. Well, twelve of them, once John and his father had joined them. The small parlour was packed solid, and reigning over it with his back-side pointing at the fireplace was a small man whose head was as bald as an egg. He was in the process of telling a story.

Over fifty years later, John couldn't remember – even if someone were to offer him a fortune in money – what Joe Dando was saying. But the image of his mother laughing merrily for the first time in ages had stayed with him, as clear as a photograph, and would do so for the rest of his life.

Joe Dando was one of those people who could make you laugh loudly at the least little thing. He was a natural character. Although he wasn't a tall man, he had a sturdy and strong-looking body, like a steel cable. And of course, his first words to John and Edward were, 'All right, butt?'

As Joe and Edward shook hands, John took in the rest of the room and realised that the six heads he'd seen earlier on top of next door's wall had now sprouted six bodies. At first he thought there were seven of them there, and then it dawned on him that one of them was his sister Magwen, sitting among the other six as if they'd been the best of friends for years – all of them sitting in a corner of the room, one large bundle of children.

'And this is Ceridwen – the missus,' said Joe Dando. John turned to see a woman seated at the table. He stared at her ...

... and stared, and stared.

John Williams had always believed that his own mother
was the loveliest woman in the world. But Ceridwen Dando
was just as beautiful as Kate, only in a different way. Kate's
hair was as yellow as newly grown wheat, while Mrs Dando's
was as dark as a raven's plumage, flowing over her shoulders
like a curly black waterfall. She was beaming at John,
revealing a mouthful of strong, white teeth.

'And these are our children.' Joe Dando pointed at one and
then the other as he introduced them all in turn. 'Jane,
Blodwen, Sean, Jemima, Little Jo ... and Billy.'

Billy was the eldest, of the same age as John and the owner of the first head that had peered over the wall. And as he smiled at John, saying 'All right, butt?' just like his father had done, little did John realise that he'd just met the boy who was to replace Whatever Next Ned as his best friend.

The School

Thank God for Billy Dando, John thought more than once during his first morning at his new school. Thanks for *all* the Dandos, in fact – apart from Little Jo, of course, who was too young to be attending school. Were it not for the Dandos, John and Magwen wouldn't have had a clue where to go or what they were meant to do once they got there.

Neither of them had been looking forward to today; it's never easy starting at a new school when you're a complete stranger to the area. But the Dandos called for them first thing that morning; Jane, Blodwen and Jemima promised to look after Magwen, while Billy and Sean were there to keep an eye on John.

'Thank heaven,' Kate said as she watched the crowd of noisy children walk away from her down the hill. She'd been dreading this morning, too. But with a bit of luck, she thought, everything would be fine.

John's new school was much larger than his old one back

home – and a good deal more English was to be heard on the yard.

John had been concerned that everyone would be staring at Magwen and him, as if they were two exotic birds that had landed in a farmyard. But he needn't have worried. If anything, hardly anyone took any notice of them whatsoever. Then it struck John that with so much coming and going, with families from all over Britain arriving here to look for work and then moving on to other pits in the area, two new faces on the schoolyard was nothing unusual.

Later in the day, however, he had the horrible feeling that someone *was* staring at him, after all. Turning suddenly, he saw that he was right: he was indeed being glared at – by a boy who looked like a rat.

'Stanley Maldoon,' Billy said, when John asked him who the boy was. Then he noticed that Stanley was scowling at John. 'What on earth have you done to him, John?'

John told him about the stone-throwing incident, and how a huge woman and an even more rat-like man had come out of the house and threatened John's father. By the time he'd finished his story, Billy Dando's eyes were like two saucers.

'Big Annie!' he exclaimed. 'That's Stanley Maldoon's mam,

that is. Oh, there are some terrible tales told about her – they say she once sorted out three colliers by herself, putting two of them in headlocks and bashing their heads together while headbutting the third man so that he was out cold.'

'Never!' But then, having seen the woman for himself, John didn't find this story too difficult to believe.

'Everyone's petrified of Big Annie and the Maldoons,' explained Billy. Then he said something strange: 'Well – everyone except Mam, that is.'

John stared at him. '*Your mother?*' he said.

But before he could quiz Billy any further, one of the teachers came out and started ringing a handbell until his face was tomato-red, summoning everyone back into the school building.

What, John wondered, had Billy meant, exactly?

By the end of their second week, John and Magwen had settled in quite well at their new school. John's teacher was a Mr Jenkins, a tall, thin man with a goatee beard and unusually long, white fingers – the longest fingers John had ever seen.

'Aye, I know,' Billy Dando said when John remarked upon Mr Jenkins's fingers to him. 'He's the only man in the whole world who can scratch his knee and pick his nose at the same time – with the same hand.'

John was relieved to discover that the lessons themselves were very similar to those at his old school, except that Mr Jenkins tended to switch back and forth between English and Welsh without warning. And when he did speak Welsh, his accent was all over the place; he might start off sounding exactly like Billy and most of the other children, but the next minute he sounded just like a *Cofi*, a local Caernarfon man.

'You see, John, my father was a very restless man,' he explained one day. 'He was never happy unless he was wandering from one place to another. Just like a gypsy – isn't that right, Billy Dando?' he said, changing his accent again and winking broadly at Billy.

'Yes, sir,' Billy replied.

John looked from the one to the other. Am I missing something here? he asked himself.

But no matter how happy and settled he felt at his new school, he was constantly aware of one niggling thorn in his side. And that particular thorn was called Stanley Maldoon.

Do you know that feeling you get when you're about to have a nasty cold? Nothing major to begin with, only a niggling suspicion that things are not quite as they should be. Perhaps you'll take some medicine or a tablet, but deep inside you know that the cold has to develop fully before it's ready to leave you. That cold must run its course, come what may.

That's how it was between John Williams and Stanley Maldoon. Something was sure to happen between them sooner or later.

John wasn't scared of him at all. Back home, he had a reputation as something of a fighter and he wasn't the type to take any nonsense from anyone. He knew he could sort out the Stanley Maldoons of this world any day of the week. But the trouble was, Stanley was never anywhere by himself. He had friends. A gang of them – a gang that seemed to John to be swelling larger and larger every day.

And just like one of those nasty colds when it gets its claws into you, Stanley Maldoon and his gang got closer and closer with each passing day.

Unknown to John, something very similar was happening at the pit between his father and Ezra Maldoon, Stanley's father. Whenever Edward saw him, there Ezra was, glaring in his direction and whispering in a sly way with a gang of other men, all of whom had a vicious look to them.

'Aye – that'll be Ezra Maldoon,' Joe Dando nodded when Edward told him about the rat-faced man.

Edward hadn't known the man's name until now. *Ezra*! he thought. God help us!

'He really doesn't like you boys from the north, you know,' Joe went on.

'I did get that impression. But why, in heaven's name?' asked Edward. 'What has north Wales ever done to him?'

'Men like Ezra Maldoon don't need a reason,' Joe said, before going on to offer a rather feeble one. 'He comes from Liverpool, I believe, and someone told me that Ezra's spent some time in a north Wales prison. More than once, I'm sure – him and that missus of his, Big Annie. Rhuthun Gaol, am I right? Or possibly Caernarfon. Done for poaching, so the story goes. But don't worry yourself, butt,' said Joe, slapping Edward's shoulder. 'He's far too much of a coward to do anything himself, you know. He has to have a gang of other boys with him, backing him up. But watch out for him, Edward. He's a sly, vicious weasel, that Ezra Maldoon. It wouldn't surprise me to find out that he encouraged that boy of his to throw those stones at John and you. That would be typical of him.'

Edward Williams nodded, vowing to do his best to keep well away from Ezra Maldoon and his cronies. But deep down he knew it was only a matter of time before something unpleasant happened. The situation made him think of a saucepan filled with water, boiling on a hob; that water was bound to boil over, and sooner rather than later.

Fisticuffs

A few days later, that's precisely what happened. John came out through the school gates to find Stanley Maldoon waiting for him, accompanied by three of his mates.

Four against one ...

John came to an abrupt halt. He could easily have turned and run off in the opposite direction, but he'd never been the type to run away from anybody. Anyway, what would be the point? That would only postpone matters, and Maldoon and his friends would be lying in wait for him the next day or the day after.

So John walked straight for them, grinning from ear to ear.

The four other boys exchanged puzzled looks. They hadn't been expecting this. All of them had anticipated seeing John turn on his heels and gallop away as fast as his feet could carry him.

'Just a minute,' John said, propping his school bag against the fence, removing his coat and folding it neatly next to his bag.

Without warning, he whirled around and delivered a wicked punch to Stanley Maldoon's nose. Stanley fell back, measuring his length on the ground and with his nose looking more like a wild red poppy than an actual nose.

His friends stared down at him in shock. None of them had ever seen anything like this before – indeed, they'd never witnessed anybody arguing with Stanley Maldoon, let alone walloping him like this. Stanley himself had had quite a shock, too; he sat up on the ground, his face white and his nose pouring blood.

One thing about Stanley Maldoon, though: he may have been a bully, but he was no coward. He got to his feet, wiped his bloody nose, and rushed at John. This succeeded in jolting the other three out of their shock. Two of them grabbed hold of John's arms while the third one held on to his legs, thus making it easier for Stanley Maldoon to pummel John's face and body.

Then they heard a voice say, 'Four against one? This isn't very fair, is it, boys?' and one of Stanley's friends turned in time to catch a glimpse of Billy Dando's fist hurtling towards his face. He let go of John's arm and staggered back, his lower lip bleeding. In doing so he tripped over the boy who was holding on to John's legs and both of them fell in a heap.

Good, thought John, that's better. Now for it! He delivered another punch to the Maldoon face, and grinned as he heard the boy's teeth clicking like castanets. Another punch, to the stomach this time, and a third to the side of Stanley's skull. Stanley fell to earth a second time, and this time showed no signs of getting back up. Meanwhile, Billy was holding one of Stanley's friends in a headlock whilst kicking the other one's backside, just as if he were kicking a rugby ball. The third friend had long since run off.

John loomed over Stanley Maldoon. 'Had enough, then?' he asked.

Stanley managed to struggle up into a sitting position. He peered up at John with a slack, stupid expression on his face.

Then he looked back down and nodded.

'Yes,' he said. 'Enough.'

He got to his feet and limped off with his two remaining friends. John realised that there was a great deal of shouting going on around him, and he and Billy turned to see a large crowd of children, all of them clapping their hands and shouting 'Hooray!'

The two friends grinned at each other.

'All right, butt?' Billy asked.

'Aye, all right, butt!' John answered.

'But we won!' John protested.

'I don't care!' Kate scolded. She was leaning over him, washing the small cuts and bruises on his face with a wet cloth and cleaning away the dried blood that had crusted around his nose and mouth. 'You shouldn't have been fighting in the first place, should you? Behaving like cannibals, out on the street like that ... '

John was on the verge of saying that cannibals were known for *eating* people, and that he'd had no intention of tucking into a human rat like Stanley Maldoon, when Edward Williams arrived home from the pit.

'Your son has been brawling,' Kate informed him without turning round.

'Ah! Yes, well ... he's not the only one, as it happens,' said Edward.

'What?'

Kate turned towards him ... and screamed. Edward Williams's face, too, was a mass of bruises and cuts; his nose was red and swollen, and his right eye was rapidly closing.

Listening to his father stammer out his tale, John understood that Edward had been fighting with another member of the Maldoon clan – namely Ezra, Stanley's father. He and his gang had set on Edward as he was leaving the colliery at the end of his shift.

'But thank heaven, Joe next door appeared from somewhere, and between us we sent them all home with their tails between their legs,' explained Edward.

'And it was Billy who helped me!' John said.

'Well, upon my soul!' exclaimed Edward. 'Thank the Lord for the Dandos, I say. Otherwise, things would have been pretty bad for both of us, wouldn't you say, son?'

A Black-haired Woman

The next day, several residents of the Huts noticed a small, uncommonly beautiful woman, whose black curls flowed over her shoulders and down her back, walk past their houses. They also noticed that her face wore a very determined expression.

She wasn't lost – oh no, she seemed to know exactly where she was going. She was aiming for the Maldoons' house, and without hesitating for even a second, she raised her fist and pounded the door loudly.

The Huts' residents were flabbergasted. Was the woman insane? Didn't she know who was living in that particular house, or have any inkling as to what was lurking on the other side of that front door? Someone should have warned her, had a quiet word in her ear, the poor innocent little thing.

But no one dared do that, not even when the woman raised her fist a second time and banged on the door again, much louder this time. An almost inhuman screech came in response from the depths of the house, and then Big Annie yanked open the door, in a foul mood and obviously ready for a fight.

But when Annie saw who was standing there, her face turned as white as chalk. She leaned against the side of the door as though she were on the verge of fainting. Then she stepped backwards, opening the door wide so that the beautiful woman could enter the house. Several of the Huts' residents swore afterwards that Big Annie was practically

curtseying before the woman as she stepped daintily over the threshold.

Big Annie closed the door.

All the watchers held their breath.

Less than five minutes later, the door opened again and the beautiful, dark-haired woman came out of the house. She had a quiet smile on her face as she walked away without once looking back over her shoulder.

Afterwards, no one saw Big Annie for over a week, and when she did begin to show her face once again, she was very quiet and subdued – and nervous, too, constantly looking over her shoulder as though she were afraid that someone was watching and following her. She'd hurry back home as soon as she could, desperate to reach the safety of her house and, without fail, took care to close, lock *and* bolt her door behind her.

The day after the dark-haired woman's visit to the Huts, two peculiar events took place – one at the pit and the other at the school.

Over supper that evening, Edward Williams said, 'Something really strange happened to me at work today.'

'Oh?' Kate said, a little coldly as she had yet to fully forgive her husband and son for brawling like two ruffians. 'And what was that, Edward? Don't tell me that an entire day passed without you getting into trouble with somebody?'

'Kate, Kate ...' sighed Edward. 'But you're not too far off the mark, as it happens. That Maldoon creature came up to me this morning – to apologise!'

'*What?*' Kate, John and Magwen all said together.

'I swear to you,' said Edward. 'He shook my hand over and over, said how truly sorry he was about everything, and if there's ever anything he can do for me in the future, any favour at all, then all I have to do is ask.'

'Good grief!' said Kate. 'I wonder what came over him?'

By now, John was itching to tell his own story. 'The same thing happened to me!' he said.

His parents looked at him.

'What – Ezra Maldoon came to the school, to apologise to you?' Edward Williams asked stupidly.

John shook his head impatiently. 'Not *him*, of course. Stanley, his son. Didn't he, Maggie? I swear it,' John insisted. 'And told me more or less the same thing as his dad told you. That he was very sorry about everything – and if anyone at school should dare to pick on Magwen or me, then all I'd have to do is tell him, and he'll soon sort them out for me.'

'Good grief!' Edward said, unconsciously echoing Kate.

'What on earth did you *do* to them?' Kate asked.

'Well ... it just goes to show, doesn't it, John?' Edward said, nudging John's shoulder. 'It takes a lot more than the Maldoons of this world to tell us Caernarfonshire boys what's what.'

Things were unusually quiet around the supper table next door at the Dandos' home, and Ceridwen had noticed how her husband and her eldest son kept glancing at each other from time to time. Something was in the air, obviously, some mischief.

'All right,' Ceridwen said at last. 'What's going on?'

Joe Dando looked at his children.

His children all looked at Joe.

Then Joe turned to Ceridwen with a half smile on his face. 'Have you, perchance, been out for a walk recently, Ceri?' he asked her.

'Hah!' Ceridwen snorted. 'And when would I ever get a chance to do any such thing, Joseph Dando?'

'Oh, it wouldn't take you long to stroll down to the Huts and back,' said Joe.

'Tell me why on God's earth would I want to go anywhere near the Huts?' Ceri asked.

She was looking down at her plate, but even though she wasn't smiling, Billy could tell that his mother's dark eyes were dancing mischievously.

'Well ...' said Joe, obviously struggling mightily himself not to smile, 'let me tell you what happened to Edward next door at work today.'

He related how Ezra Maldoon had approached Edward and apologised to him.

'Never!' said Ceridwen, but she too was having difficulty keeping a straight face.

'And Stanley Maldoon came up to John at school and apologised to *him*,' Billy said.

'Did he really?' exclaimed Ceridwen.

'Odd, or what?' said Joe. 'And there's more. I was walking home today with Dai Hopkin. Of course, Dai lives down the Huts, Ceri, as you know.'

'Does he?' Ceridwen's eyes opened wide. 'Joseph, I haven't a clue who lives down the Huts and who doesn't.'

Joe shut his eyes: he was on the verge of bellowing with laughter. 'And Dai was saying how his missus had seen someone call at Annie Maldoon's house. A lovely looking woman, according to Dai – with black, curly hair.'

'Indeed?' Ceridwen said, the picture of innocence.

'Yes – indeed,' Joe said. 'So I asked myself, I wonder if my sweet little Ceri popped down there to have a word with Big Annie? One gypsy to another, as it were.'

'Annie Maldoon is no Romany, Joseph,' Ceridwen said sharply, glaring at her husband. 'Her father was nothing more than a tinker, without a single drop of true Romany blood in his entire body.'

'Maybe so,' said Joe. 'But what about Big Annie's mother? And I'm sure that Annie herself is enough of a gypsy to be scared witless when a *real* Romany calls round to have a quiet word with her. Perhaps even threatening to curse her unless she behaves herself ... am I right, Ceri?'

Ceridwen stood and started gathering up the dirty dishes. 'Joseph Dando, I swear I've no idea where you get your daft ideas from, man!' she said, exiting for the scullery.

That's when Joe Dando couldn't hold it in any longer and started laughing his head off.

'Dad, what's the matter?' asked Jane.

She turned to Billy, but her big brother was also rocking with laughter by now ... because he'd caught a glimpse of the wink his mother had cast at his father as she left the room.

Part 2

THE BLACK CLOUD

Looking Forward

Spring 1913

When he was thirteen years old, John Williams left school and started work at the colliery.

He'd been looking forward tremendously to that important day – to finally be able to walk down the hill with his father and the other miners, being one of them at last, and to walk back up the hill with them at the end of his shift, black from head to foot and tired out after a hard day's work.

As the big day loomed closer, however, John began to get the distinct feeling that no one else in his family was looking forward to seeing him start at the colliery.

'More work for Mam and me – that's what it'll mean for us,' was Magwen's frequent grumble, 'what with you and Dad trailing coal dust through the house after you, wherever you go.'

By now, Magwen was ten years old, and it has to be said that she had quite a high opinion of herself. Indeed, John often thought, anyone would think that she was the daughter of the local manor house! She'd inherited her mother's gorgeous fair hair and would spend hours brushing it until it shone.

'If you spent as much time sweeping the floor as you do brushing your hair, this house would be as clean as a new pin,' her father said jokingly to her one day.

Both mother and daughter turned on him like two lionesses. 'Hoy! This house *is* as clean as a new pin, Edward Williams,' said Kate, 'despite all your efforts to turn it into something resembling a pig sty!'

'Or a coal shed,' added Magwen. 'Look at the shine on that grate – look at it! No thanks to you. I'm the one who has to sweat hard every day to keep it clean. Well ... me and Mam, of course,' she added grudgingly.

She wasn't exaggerating, either. Keeping the grate clean was a difficult chore. The grate or range was split into three parts: the fireplace itself was in the middle, flanked by the boiler on one side and the oven on the other. The whole thing needed to be scrubbed hard with black lead, otherwise it would soon begin to rust. Kate made her own black lead with white spirit and linseed oil, before rubbing it into every inch of the range and then polishing it until it shone *fel swllt* – like a shilling, as Kate liked to say.

But the way Magwen sometimes talked, anyone listening to her would think that she was solely responsible for keeping the house clean. To be fair, John had also done his share. Before he'd started working at the pit, one of his tasks had been to carry cold water from the scullery tap to the kitchen and pour it into the boiler on the range, because his father was in dire need of a hot bath as soon as he got home from work.

'Who's going to be doing this once I start work?' John asked Magwen one day.

'It won't be you, will it?' she snapped. 'Me, no doubt. Well – me and Mam. As if we didn't have enough to do around here as it is.'

Kate, too, was tiring of Magwen's constant grumbling and gave her a good scolding one day. 'Be glad that there's only the four of us living here, young lady!' she exclaimed. 'How would you like to live at Tommy Price's house? Yes – exactly! So think on.'

Tommy Price was, along with Edward, a member of the miners' male voice choir, and he and his wife Elizabeth had nine children. Eight of them were boys, and the eldest three worked alongside their father down the pit. Tommy and

Elizabeth's eldest child – Dora, their only daughter – already looked more like a mother than a sister to her younger brothers, while their actual mother could easily be mistaken for their grandmother. The thought that one day she might resemble Dora Price was enough to silence Magwen's moans for a while.

Mam's right, though, thought John – we *are* lucky. Edward and Kate would sometimes discuss taking in a lodger to help with the rent, but Edward wasn't too keen on the idea. He'd been lodging with another family when he first came down here to work, and hadn't enjoyed the experience all that much.

'We'll do it if we absolutely have to,' he said, 'but not until then. Let's hope the need doesn't arise, and that W.J. Pareeee doesn't take it into his head to raise the rent.'

John knew that the Dandos next door had to share beds – the three girls in one bed and the three boys in another – with one of each trio sleeping with his or her head at the foot of the bed, and a blanket hanging from a rope providing some privacy between the two beds. He also knew that several other families were so large that there wasn't enough room at home for them all to be there at the same time during the day, and that the older daughters often had to go and live with relatives.

'I'll be able to help with the rent now, Mam,' John said one day, in the hope that this would make Kate feel better. She wasn't at all looking forward to seeing John start work at the pit, and she'd made that crystal clear.

And now, all she did was smile her tight little smile and change the subject – something she did whenever John mentioned working at the colliery.

On the evening before he was due to start at the pit, John's father said to him: 'Come on, 'ngwas i, how about you and I taking a little stroll up the mountain, eh?'

It was a pleasant spring evening, and swallows darted back and forth above their heads as they climbed up the hillside path.

'Well?' said Edward, after he and John had settled themselves on a large rock that looked down over the village and the colliery. 'How d'you feel?'

'Like I've just eaten a large bowlful of spiders,' answered John.

Edward Williams smiled quietly. 'That, I can believe,' he said.

'But at the same time, I'm also looking forward to tomorrow,' John added hastily. 'Very much.'

'Are you really?'

'Yes!'

'Oh ...' said Edward. 'Well, I suppose that's good – a good thing. Because we do have quite a few laughs down the pit, you know. Some of the lads can be right characters.'

'The *butties*, don't you mean, Dad?'

'Yes – the butties,' Edward nodded, smiling. 'And they're good fellows, all of them. They'd do anything for you. But d'you know what? When I first came down here, I wasn't looking forward one tiny bit to *my* first day down the mine. If anything, John, just thinking about it made me feel sick to the pit of my stomach. The thing is, you see ... I was *scared*.'

John gaped at his father. 'Scared? *You?*'

He'd always believed that his father was the world's bravest man, and the thought of him being scared of anything was ... was ... well, totally ridiculous.

'Indeed I was,' said Edward. 'The very thought of plummeting down into the depths of the earth used to bring me out in a cold sweat. And then the thought of being stuck there, in the darkness, hour after hour after hour ... The thing was, you see, up until then I had spent all my working life – and most of my childhood – out in the open air, hadn't I, either at the quarry or helping your grandfather on his little farm.'

He sat quietly for a while, staring down at the colliery. But something told John that his father wasn't seeing the pit at all; instead, he was seeing the sheer grey walls of the slate quarry back home, and the dry stone walls that surrounded the farm, with little white tufts of wool stuck in the cracks and waving gently in the mountain breeze.

Edward shook himself. 'But you know what? After a couple of weeks, I was fine about it – champion! What it is, you see, we colliers – because that's what I am now, and that's what *you'll* be from tomorrow onwards – we look out for one another. That's the true meaning of *butty* – a friend who works alongside you and who'll look out for you, no matter what. So if you can prove that you're more than ready to become a "butty", you'll be champion, too.'

He got to his feet.

'Right, 'ngwas i, we'd best me making tracks for home.' He grinned down at his son. 'All right, butty boy?'

'All right, butt!' answered John.

The First Day

There were two pits at Senghennydd Colliery, the York Pit and the Lancaster Pit. John was put to work at the Lancaster Pit, alongside his father. The two of them left the house in the early morning, and as he walked down the hill with the other colliers, all those pairs of boots making a sound that reminded him of a heavy hailstorm on a zinc roof, he knew that Kate and Magwen were watching him walk away, and that Kate's eyes had that familiar wet shine to them once again.

'Everything all right, John?' his father asked him as they squeezed into the cage that was to take them down into the belly of the earth.

'Champion ...' John cleared his throat. Thinking of his mother's shining eyes had brought a huge lump to his throat. 'Aye, champion,' he said again. 'But it's a bit cramped in here, isn't it?'

'Aye, that's true. These old cages were originally designed to carry the coal trucks – the "drams" – up and down. The full ones up, the empty drams back down. They've always been more important than us men, you see.'

Us men! At last, thought John, I am one of *us men*! He felt himself smile broadly for the first time since setting out from the house.

One of the first things John saw underground was ... a horse.

Of course, he already knew about the pit ponies – that over 17,000 of them were in use in the south Wales coal mines – but coming face to face with one of them underground like this, for the first time, was still a strange experience.

'Aye, I know,' said Edward when John mentioned this to him. 'Horses are open-air animals, aren't they? Things would be pretty tough on us down here without them, though.'

John's job was to load the drams with lumps of coal from the floor of the mine. His father showed him how to use the curling box, something that looked like a three-sided bucket with two side-handles, like two ears.

'You use it to scoop up the coal,' Edward explained. 'That's a lot easier than picking up each individual lump with your bare hands. You'd be here for ages trying to fill just one dram. But don't rush it – take your time. Believe you me, by the time you finish tonight, your back will be aching as it is.'

During the day John was introduced to many of the other colliers, but he knew full well that, were he to clap eyes on them again at the end of his shift, in broad daylight, he wouldn't have a clue who was who. It was so dark down the pit that all John could make of anyone was a vague shape, lit only by the dim glow of his lamp, and a voice saying, 'All right, butt?'

But there were other voices, too, coming at him from the gloom: voices couched in north Walian accents, greeting him familiarly and teasingly, asking if his mam had sent him down here to keep an eye on Edward and make sure that the scamp behaved himself. Many of them had come down south in search of work after John and his family had arrived here, from places like Trawsfynydd and Blaenau Ffestiniog, as well as from John's home county of Caernarfonshire – all ex-quarrymen, like Edward Williams.

Hearing these voices never failed to fill John with that old sense of *hiraeth* – of longing for his old home and especially for Whatever Next Ned. I wonder what old Ned is up these days? he often thought to himself as that first day sped by. If only he could see me now! I know exactly what he'd say, too. Yes – *whatever next?*

And down there, in the crushing darkness of the coal mine, John Williams could see, clearly in his mind, his best friend standing in the railway siding and raising his arm in a half-wave before turning away and walking off in the sunshine ...

'Everything all right, John?'

John jumped. The bending down, scooping up, straightening and then pouring the coal into the drams was monotonous work and John had been daydreaming.

Edward Williams took a piece of chalk from his pocket and drew his mark on the side of the dram. 'This is for the check-weigh-man,' he announced.

'The what?' John asked.

'Oh, there's an important man for you!' explained Edward. '*The check-weigh-man*,' he repeated slowly. 'We all pay him two shillings every fortnight. He waits up on the surface for the drams. It's his job to make a note of whoever each dram belongs to – hence the mark – and then to ensure that each load of coal is carefully weighed. That way, none of us colliers gets cheated out of any money. That's got to be worth a shilling a week, wouldn't you say?'

John nodded. Along with many other terms and phrases,

he'd already heard about these check-weigh-men. But being here underground made them all seem more *real*, somehow, more alive – and in a strange way, almost as if he were hearing about them for the first time. Like the names for all the dangerous gases that could be encountered down the mines. These gases were what the miners feared the most, because they were so sly and could affect you before you even realised they were there. One of these was the *Choke Damp*; like its name suggested, this gas could choke you. Then there was the *Fire Damp*, a gas that could explode like a bomb. And then there was the *After Damp*, which came in the wake of an explosion, to suffocate you – so if the explosion hadn't managed to kill you, then the *After Damp* would be sure to come along and finish the job.

Another thing the colliers had to be wary of was something called the *staggers*. This was a severe form of light-headedness, a strange giddiness that made you feel dizzy – indeed, many men would faint or experience blackouts quite regularly. This was caused by working for hours on end with nothing but the faint glow of their lamps to relieve the cloying darkness that surrounded them.

John tried his best not to think of such nasty things. He remembered what Billy Dando had told him: 'The best thing to do is forget all about them and just get on with the job in hand. Otherwise, thinking about them all the time is enough to drive a man bonkers, butt.'

Billy had been to assigned to the other pit, the York Pit, and when John returned to the surface at the end of his shift, there was Billy waiting for him.

'Well? How'd it all go, then?' he asked before John could even step out of the cage.

Stepping out into daylight after having spent so long in

almost pitch darkness was a strange experience. It took a minute or two for his eyes to get used to the light. He grinned at Billy, his teeth looking whiter than ever in his blackened face.

'Aye, champion, butt!'

Despite being tired out, and even though every muscle in his body seemed to be aching, John had difficulty sleeping that night. His mind insisted on reliving every minute of his exciting day, over and over.

He tried his best not to think of accidents and gases and the staggers, but despite his best efforts, he found himself thinking of some of the stories he'd heard about the pit during his days at school. That each coal mine, for instance, housed giant rats, some of them as large as calves, with sharp teeth and red eyes bulging with blood. That the Lancaster Pit was home to a creature that was half-man and half-wolf, and woe betide any collier who lingered down there by himself, because it was then that this creature would pounce and drag the hapless collier off to the darkest depths of the mine.

'Rubbish! Nothing but nonsense!' John said to himself.

But he'd also heard that the ghosts of the miners killed in the 1901 accident were still there, roaming the underground passages, sighing and whispering amongst themselves as they searched vainly for a way out and back to the surface.

Somehow, it wasn't so easy to dismiss that particular story.

Bad Dreams

October 1913

The spring melted into summer, summer into autumn. By then John had long given up thinking about giant rats and men who were half-wolves. And even though he hadn't forgotten about the gases, he'd taught himself not to think too much about them.

On the way to work one morning, John noticed that Billy Dando was unusually quiet. Normally, he'd have been chatting away nineteen to the dozen. 'A right chatterbox, that one, if ever I've seen one,' Kate often remarked.

'Are you feeling all right?' John asked him.

Billy sighed. 'Aye, I suppose so,' he said. 'But … well, to be honest, I'm a bit worried about Mam, see.'

Even though it was only the first week of October, John noticed that the wind had a nasty, cold edge to it. Winter was already sharpening its teeth.

'What's the matter with her?' he asked.

Billy looked at him. 'Don't tell me you haven't *heard* her,

John,' he said. 'At night. Screaming the house down.'

'Ah well ... er ... yes, I have, to be honest,' John answered.

Truth be told, only a deaf person could have failed to hear Ceridwen Dando screaming through the walls. The first time it happened, a little over a week ago, Kate had leapt out of her bed in fright. 'What in heaven's name is that little man *doing* to her?' she'd said. 'Is he murdering her, or something?'

Of course, Joe Dando was doing no such thing. 'She was having a nightmare,' he explained to Edward the following morning. 'Don't worry, Ceri gets them from time to time. She says to tell you she's sorry if she woke you up.'

'Good God, don't you fret about that, man!' Edward said to him, but he'd had the uncomfortable feeling that Joe hadn't told him *everything*. After all, they'd been next door neighbours now for some years, and this was the first he'd heard of Ceridwen having bad dreams. Certainly, neither Edward nor anyone else in his family had ever heard Ceridwen screaming like that before.

The same thing happened again two nights later. Then it became a nightly occurrence – always during the small hours of the morning. By then, Kate was worried sick about poor Ceridwen.

'We'd better not mention it until they feel ready to say something to us about it,' decided Edward, warning John and Magwen not to broach the subject with any of the Dando children.

But today Billy had finally decided to discuss the matter with John, so John felt he'd had some sort of permission to quiz his friend about it.

'What does she dream about, then?' he asked.

'That's just it, I don't rightly know,' sighed Billy. 'Mam's not that sure herself, to tell you the truth. Just that she's somewhere outside, some wide open space – a field, or a beach, somewhere like that – and that something really terrible is chasing her.'

'Hell,' said John. 'That's what I call a nightmare. What exactly is it, d'you know? This thing that's after her?'

'A big black cloud,' explained Billy. 'But, John – she gets the same dream every night, exactly the same dream. Except ... except that the cloud gets closer and closer to her each time.'

Toothache

By the end of that week, Ceridwen Dando wasn't the only one to have trouble sleeping.

Kate had already noticed, a few days earlier, that Edward had taken to chewing his food slowly and carefully; he was also taking pains to chew using only the right side of his mouth.

'Have you got toothache, Edward?'

'Oh, nothing to worry about. It'll have gone again in a few days, you'll see,' answered her husband. 'That's how it's always been with me, isn't it? It comes and then it goes again.'

Not this time, though. Yes, the toothache had come – but it was showing no signs of departing. If anything, it grew worse with each passing day. Poor Edward hardly slept a wink over the weekend.

'It's exactly as if somebody were shoving a red-hot needle into it,' he complained, 'and the pain shoots through my entire body with each beat of my heart. D'you know what? All night, I was within an inch of banging my head against the doorpost, if only to experience a different kind of pain.'

Come Monday evening, his left cheek had swollen hideously and he kept shivering all the time, like a jelly, even though his forehead felt hot to the touch and was shiny with sweat. Kate popped next door and asked Ceridwen to call round to have a look at him; she came immediately, her and Joe. None of the Dandos were hardly ever ill, as Ceridwen knew about all sorts of medicines, all made from the different wild plants and herbs that grew around Senghennydd.

'You really should have told me about this long before now,' she scolded when she saw the state poor Edward was in. 'A few days ago, I might well have been able to do something to help him. A string of barley tied around a stone, and the stone thrown into the river ...'

'*What?*' Kate exclaimed.

'Or a sprig of wild garlic placed on the tooth ...' Ceridwen shook her head. 'Too late for all that now,' she said. She placed her fingertips against Edward's swollen cheek. 'This isn't just any old toothache now. This is what my mother used to call *blood toothache*.'

Edward stared at her, alarmed. 'What the devil is that?'

'Poison from your infected tooth has seeped into your bloodstream, Edward,' said Ceridwen. 'That's why you're

shivering like you are, while sweating at the same time. What's the proper term for it, too? Oh, yes – an *abscess*, that's what it is.'

She turned to Kate. 'I can't do anything for him now, I'm afraid. The best thing he can do is go to Caerffili first thing tomorrow to see the dentist.'

'What – and lose a day's work?' Edward protested. 'And fork out at least two shillings ...?'

'Better to lose two shillings than your life, Edward, love,' said Kate.

Ceridwen gave her a sharp look, but Kate was too concerned about her husband to notice.

But John noticed.

'You see, butt? You haven't a lot of choice,' said Joe. 'You won't be able to work in that state, anyhow.'

'Can't you ask your partner to work a double shift?' asked Ceridwen.

Occasionally, if one of the colliers had to lose a day's work for some reason or another, then his partner would work two shifts and hand over the money to the one who'd been off work. The absentee would then pay him back by doing him the same favour. That was just one way the butties had of looking out for one another.

But Edward was shaking his head. 'It's Moc Morgan,' he said.

'And he doesn't live in Senghennydd,' Joe explained to Kate, 'so it's far too late to ask him tonight. Look, Edward – I'll tell you what. Why don't I work your shift for you tomorrow, in the Lancaster? Will Watkins, my butty, won't mind doing a double shift.'

'Heavens, I can't ask you to do that, Joe,' said Edward.

'But you're *not* asking, butt, are you?' asked Joe. 'I offered, if I remember. Fine – that's settled. I'll see you tomorrow, John, all right?'

'Thanks, Joe,' Edward said weakly.

After the Dandos had departed, Magwen said, 'Didn't Ceridwen look poorly?'

'Well, she hasn't had much sleep lately, has she?' said Kate.

'Neither have I – thanks to her screaming like a madwoman night after night.'

'Oh, be quiet, Magwen, can't you!'

Everyone looked at John in amazement. He felt himself blush. 'Well, fair play,' he went on to explain, 'Ceridwen's been having bad dreams for weeks, every night, so little wonder that she's not looking well. And you hardly ever wake up, in any case. You're too busy snoring through it all.'

'I do not snore!' Magwen argued.

'Yes, you do,' replied John. 'Like some old sow.'

'All right, John, that'll do,' scolded Kate. 'And you, too, Magwen. Please remember that your poor father's in great pain.' She turned to Edward. 'My poor lamb ... I take it you are going to see that dentist tomorrow, then?'

Edward nodded glumly. 'I don't seem to have much choice, do I?' He looked at John. 'Will you be all right without me there tomorrow, son?'

'Me? Yes, of course,' answered John. 'I'll be champion.'

The Black Day

The bedroom was still dark when Ceridwen woke up early on the Tuesday morning.

But what was that strange feeling she had?

A ... nice feeling, somehow.

Then she realised what it was. For the first time in many days – within weeks, more accurately – she'd had a good night's sleep. No bad dreams – no dreams of any kind, as far as she could tell. No fear, no terror, and no screams.

Oh, it really *was* a good feeling!

She turned to cuddle up to her husband, but Joe wasn't there. Where on earth was he? Had he already got up? Then Ceridwen became aware that she could hear his voice, coming from the street outside, immediately underneath her bedroom window.

What time is it? thought Ceridwen, in a panic.

Then she heard Joe's feet come up the stairs and into the bedroom.

'Joe,' Ceridwen said, 'what's wrong?'

'Sshh, it's all right, nothing's wrong,' Joe whispered. 'I was just wishing Edward the best of luck with that dentist chap, that's all. He's just left for the train. I wouldn't exchange places with him for all the tea in China, Ceri!'

'But ... isn't it time to get up? It's sure to be ...'

It was difficult to tell these days, as the early mornings were so dark. Ceridwen began to get out of bed, only to feel Joe's hands pushing her back down.

'It's all right, it's fine,' he whispered. 'I've got breakfast ready for Billy and myself, and you've already sorted out the tommy-bags, last night.' Each collier had his own tommy-bag, where they kept their lunches. 'And last night, Mrs Dando, was the first decent night's sleep you've had since ... oh, since Little Jo was in petticoats, wasn't it? So don't you dare get out of that bed for a good while yet.'

Ceridwen could now just about make out his dim shape in the darkness.

'Listen,' he said to her. 'Remember that I'll be at the Lancaster Pit today, with the lad next door, while Edward's being tortured to death by that dentist.'

Ceridwen felt a strange, unpleasant chill flood her entire body, for some reason. I hope I'm not heading for a cold, she thought.

'Will our Billy be all right?' she asked.

'Oh, don't you worry your head about our Billy, he'll be fine with Will Watkins and the other York Pit boys.' He kissed her forehead. 'Right – see you at tea time.'

Ceri watched his shape move towards the door.

'Joe ...' she said.

'Yes, love?'

'Oh ... nothing.' Yes, she really was feeling better today, for the first time since the close of summer. 'Nothing,' she said again. 'Just be careful, that's all.'

'Who me? 'Course I will.'

Ceridwen remained in bed long after she heard Joe and Billy leave the house, then lay there listening to the other children getting up and dressing. Joe had probably warned them all to leave her be this morning. Good old Joe, she thought, but I can't stay here all morning, like some old hen on her nest.

Especially as it was now daylight.

She rose and parted the curtains, feeling as though she'd been cured of a long illness. Pulling on her dressing gown, she went downstairs. Blodwen, her eldest daughter, was carrying a bowl of water through from the scullery; all the other children were seated around the table.

'Your lazy old mother's finally decided to get up …' Ceridwen started to speak, before realising that Blodwen was staring at her in horror.

'What's the matter?'

Blodwen let out a loud scream and dropped the bowl, which shattered on the floor, throwing water in all directions.

But none of her brothers and sisters even glanced at her – they were all staring at their mother with the same look of horror on their faces. Ceridwen's beautiful dark hair – hair that last night was blacker than a mountain raven's plumage – had turned completely white.

'And where's your father today?'

The Official peered at John as if he expected to see Edward peeping out at him from one of John's pockets.

John explained about the abscess.

'Toothache?' said the Official. 'Well, I already knew that you lot from the north were a strange bunch, but I never realised you dug the coal out with your teeth.'

John looked at him, bemused. Was the man trying to be funny, or just being nasty?

The two bankers – the pithead supervisors – had been listening to this. 'Leave the lad alone,' one of them shouted at the Official. 'I've had one of them abscess things myself, and it's no picnic, I can tell you.'

'Quite so,' the second banker agreed. 'It would do *you* good to experience it yourself,' he said to the Official. 'Maybe then you'd be more sympathetic towards other people.'

The Official didn't like this. He drew a large cross next to Edward's name. 'We don't dole out wages to people who stay at home because of a little bit of pain.' Then he peered at Joe Dando. 'Dando,' he said, 'shouldn't you be at the York Pit?'

'I'm helping the lad here while his dad's having his tooth seen to,' said Joe. 'If that's all right with you?'

'Well, I'm not too sure about that ...' began the Official, but the two bankers were still listening.

''Course it's all right!' one of them called over.

'Quite so!' concurred the second banker. 'Some people have to make a big fuss over nothing.'

His face now as purple as a plum, the Official nodded at Joe and John and made a note in his book. Joe threw John a wink and the two of them stepped into the cage. As the cage began to descend, the last thing John saw was the Official's cross face, still purple with embarrassment, as the two bankers continued to deflate his self-importance.

Neither he nor Joe saw the woman with the long white hair arrive at the colliery gates, out of breath and her eyes full of terror.

Ceridwen knew that several people had stared at her oddly –

her, the strange-looking woman with her snowy white hair flying in all directions, running barefoot through the streets in her nightgown as if she'd escaped from somewhere – but she didn't care a jot about them. *She had to get to the colliery in time, before ... before ...*

Before what?

That was the trouble – she didn't *know*. All she knew was that she had to run here, dressed as she was. But now that she was here standing outside the gates, she realised that she didn't have a clue what to say to anyone, or how to reply were anyone to ask her what she was doing here.

As she was thinking all this, someone's shadow fell across her face.

She glanced up. 'Annie?' said Ceridwen.

Big Annie nodded. She, too, had a wild look to her – even wilder than usual – and she was panting like some old steam engine as she tried to get her breath back.

'Do *you* know why you've come here, Annie?' Ceridwen asked.

Big Annie blinked down at her, looking as though she were still half asleep. Then she shook her head.

'I don't,' she said. 'Only that ... that I *had* to ...'

Ceridwen nodded, thinking: This one's got more Romany blood in her than I'd given her credit for. She held out her hand, and with a grateful little smile, Big Annie clasped it tightly.

Then another shadow fell over Ceridwen and when she looked up this time, she saw that a huge black cloud had filled the sky above Senghennydd, blotting out the sun.

The very same cloud that had been pursuing her in her nightmares for weeks on end.

Then the two women felt the ground shake beneath their feet.

The two bankers – named Jack and John – were laughing as they watched the pompous little official trying to muster up some dignity whilst walking away from them.

'He looks like a tomato with legs!' commented Jack.

John was about to answer with another 'Quite so' when they saw the official come to an abrupt stop; he seemed to rock from side to side before falling to the ground. At the same instant, they too felt the ground shift under their feet.

'What the hell ...?' Jack started to say.

A second later came an explosion – exactly as if the earth itself was vomiting. The bang that followed this was ten times louder than the loudest thunderclap anyone had ever heard before. It was heard throughout the whole district – even as far as Caerffili, where Edward Williams had just had his tooth extracted and was telling himself that he never, ever, wanted to experience such agony again.

The explosion was strong enough to hurl the iron cage

back up the shaft, and who knows how far up it would have shot had it not collided with the big wheel. The cage itself exploded as it encountered the winding gear ...

The last thing Jack the banker saw before he himself was hurled off his feet and blown yards away by a tremendously hot wind, was a massive chunk of iron shooting free, like a flying axe, and severing his friend's head from his shoulders.

People poured out of every house in Senghennydd. Most of them were women – wives, mothers, grandmothers, sisters, cousins, nieces and daughters. Women of all ages and shapes, but on this most terrible of mornings they all had one thing in common: they all felt the same terror.

They ran towards the colliery as fast as their feet could carry them, many of them wearing next to nothing, others wearing whatever item of clothing came to hand first.

Ceridwen and Big Annie were the first to arrive at the pit.

'What's happened?' Ceridwen screamed at an official who was hurrying past them.

The harrassed official seemed about to carry on his way, ignoring them, but then he paused long enough to say, 'An explosion – down in the Lancaster Pit.'

Lancaster ... oh, thank God, thought Ceridwen: both Billy and Joe are working the York Pit ...

Joe! With a jolt, Ceridwen remembered that Joe, just as he left the darkened bedroom that morning, had said that he was stepping into Edward Williams's shoes for the day. *That he'd be working in the Lancaster Pit!* She turned towards Big Annie, who was gazing in horror at the entrance to the Lancaster Pit, her normally ruddy face now drained of colour and as white as though someone had been rubbing flour into her flesh.

Immediately, Ceridwen understood that Ezra Maldoon, too, was working the Lancaster Pit – along with his son, Stanley, the stone-thrower.

Ceridwen heard someone calling out her name, and turned to see Katie and Magwen hurrying towards her.

'Where's the explosion?' Katie asked. 'Which pit? Ceridwen! *In which pit?*'

And she came very close to fainting on the spot as she saw the answer written clearly on Ceridwen Dando's face.

John opened his eyes.

At least, he *thought* he did. Because of the black, impenetrable darkness around him, it was impossible to tell whether his eyes were open or not. Imagine what it's like when you press the palms of your hands tightly over your eyes – and then someone ties a black cloth over your hands, before placing a black velvet bag over your head. The darkness that surrounded John Williams was even deeper than that.

Where was he?

He realised that he was, for some strange reason, lying flat on his back, and he thought: Good grief, what am I *doing*, lying down on the job like this when I should be working?

He tried to move, but his head was hurting terribly so he decided to remain still for a little while, just until his head felt a little better. Truth be told, he felt quite comfortable, lying on his back like this.

In the darkness.

Five more minutes, he thought.

Just five more minutes ...

John closed his eyes.

Like most of the men who were working down the York Pit that morning, Billy Dando had no idea that anything had happened. They were all told to drop tools and return to the surface; it was only then they realised that a terrible accident had occurred in the Lancaster Pit.

He received a dreadful shock, then, when he arrived at the surface. The colliery was teeming with people, men rushing wildly in all directions, and dozens – no, hundreds – of women standing everywhere in clusters, with more and yet more people flooding in through the gates.

That's when Billy heard of the massive explosion that had taken place inside the Lancaster Pit – which had almost four hundred men working in it.

And one of them, he remembered, feeling as if a wild horse had just kicked him in the stomach, was his father.

'Billy! *Billy!*'

He turned to see some mad woman screaming his name whilst trying her best to shove her way to him through the crowd. Who the hell is this? he wondered. A woman whose hair was as white as freshly fallen mountain snow … yet she had a young face, too young for all that white hair. She should have an old face, weathered and wrinkled …

Then he realised she was *his mother.*

'*Mam?*' he gasped.

Finally, Ceridwen reached him. She wrapped her arms

around him and squeezed him tightly to her. Then she shoved him away from her and stared into his eyes.

'Your dad!' she pleaded. 'Please tell me that ... tell me he's changed his mind about working with young John next door?'

Even though Billy's face was black with coal dust, Ceridwen could see him turn pale.

Billy felt sick to his stomach, his legs having suddenly turned into two columns of wet clay. He turned slowly to

gaze towards the Lancaster Pithead and saw how the iron cage had mangled the winding gear. And if the explosion had been strong enough to do *that*, then what sort of hell was bubbling away underground, in the darkest depths of the pit itself?

'Oh, Dad ...' he whispered. 'Dad ...'

John's head was still aching and the darkness surrounding him was as black as ever. Also, his mouth felt full of something, as though someone had stuffed an old, dirty cloth inside it. Then he realised it was dust – coal dust. He could feel it crunching between his teeth.

He turned his head, retching and spitting.

What on earth had happened?

He couldn't remember ... Oh, wait a minute! He had a vague memory of squatting down behind the dram, then of feeling a hot wind blow over him before someone – someone incredibly strong – had snatched him up from his squat and flung him with all his might against one of the wooden posts that supported the roof.

That was the last thing he remembered before coming to, lying flat on his back. Oh – and how Joe Dando had just begun to tell him a story about two old brothers, one of whom had a wooden leg ...

Joe!

John tried to sit up, only to knock his head against something hard.

'Aww!' he croaked. The coal dust had invaded his throat as well and he began to cough. He'd have given the world right now for a drink of cool water. He carefully lifted his hands up in front of his face and felt about him.

Iron!

What the hell ...?

Then he realised that he was groping the side of the dram. No wonder it had hurt when he'd banged his head against it. That hot wind must have blown the dram over, too, because as he ran his hands over the iron, John found that the little truck was lying on its side and leaning against the wooden post.

Good God, he thought. The post must have prevented the dram from falling over and on top of me. The drams may well have been little trucks – compared with the larger ones that carried the coal to Cardiff and around the country – but they were extremely heavy. Had this dram landed on top of him, then John would have been crushed into the earth like a cockroach under someone's boot heel.

Lord above, he thought, I was lucky!

But what about Joe Dando?

'Joe ...?'

His voice sounded to him like the croaking of an old crow. He coughed again, spitting out more coal dust.

'Joe?'

Better. Louder. But no reply came from the darkness around him. John felt the fear and panic rush through his body. Was he all alone here, down in the bowels of the earth?

Dear God, had he been buried alive?

'Joe!' he shouted, hearing his voice swollen with terror. 'Joe – answer me! Mr Dando! *Joe!*'

Nothing – only the sound of more coal dust falling from the roof and the walls, like sugar being poured out of a paper bag. He could feel the hot tears burning his eyes ...

'*Stop it, John Williams!*' he said to himself. '*Don't you dare cry like a baby – d'you hear me? You're alive and uninjured, apart from a slight headache ...*'

He ran his hands over his body. His arms seemed all right, at any rate – but what of his legs, and his feet? Yes, they were hurting, but at least he was able to move them – even if they did feel as though half a dozen men had been kicking them with hob-nailed boots.

He managed to turn and get up to all fours. He'd been lying on a small heap of coal, he now realised: large lumps with sharp edges, like teeth. He could feel them now, digging into his hands and knees.

Feeling his way along the side of the dram, he understood that the truck was lying at an angle, and that there was a gap between the side of the dram and the wooden support post. It wasn't a large gap, but John managed to squeeze through it.

If only I had some light, he thought. *Even the tiniest flame would be wonderful.*

'Joe …?' he said again. 'Joe …?'

No reply.

The sheer darkness made him afraid to move. God alone knew what was waiting for him in the blackness – waiting to bite him, to hit him, to kick him.

'Joe?'

Nothing.

He was here by himself, and had never in his life felt so lonely. He sat on the ground, surrounded by lumps of coal of all shapes and sizes, with his forehead resting against his knees.

'Mam ...' he whimpered. 'Mam ...'

'Where's the rescue team?'

Up on the surface, these words were on everyone's lips. Magwen saw there was a great deal of confusion at the entrance to the Lancaster Pit; no one seemed to know what they were meant to do next.

'Where's the rescue team?'

And yet, there was a good deal of activity going on there as well, with men running back and forth carrying wooden boards and blankets and the occasional stretcher.

Oh, John, John ... Magwen thought.

'Living with you two is like living with a cat and a dog!' Kate frequently used to complain, as Magwen and John seemed to do nothing but tease and annoy each other when they weren't actually quarrelling.

'It's him – he's getting on my nerves!' was Magwen's protest, voiced several times a day. But now she'd have given the world to see her big brother striding towards her, to feel him tug her clean hair with his filthy fingers, to hear him call her Maggie once again.

She was standing with her mother, the two of them holding each other tightly. Kate's eyes were fixed on the pit entrance, and her face – like the faces of all the women standing there – as white as a sheet, her features looking as if they'd collapsed, making her eyes seem inordinately huge.

But I look just like that too, I must do, thought Magwen, and then realised that she was praying quietly: *Oh-please-God-and-Jesus-Christ-look-after-our-John ...*

Then she heard someone say one word, a word that filled everyone there with even more fear. And she thought – this is the first time ever that this little word has made me feel cold all over.

And that word was ... *fire.*

John raised his head off his knees. He could have sworn he'd just heard an unexpected sound coming from somewhere in the darkness.

The sound of someone groaning.

'Hello?'

He listened. Nothing – bar that uncomfortable rustling sound as yet more coal dust fell around him like dry rain.

I must have imagined it, he decided. I so much wanted to

believe there was someone else here with me that my imagination created that groaning sound.

He wiped his forehead, then realised that his shirt was wet. How ...?

He was sweating, that's why – sweating like a pig. Because it was *hot* down here.

Strange. It was usually cold underground, even on a hot summer's day, and the men often had to move and work just to keep warm.

Then John heard the sound of groaning once again.

There *was* someone else down here! He wasn't imagining things after all! And the sound seemed to be coming from somewhere close by him, too.

'Joe?' he said again. 'Joe?'

He went back on all fours and began crawling gingerly over the floor of the pit, trying not to think of the tiny pieces of coal that dug into his hands and legs as he moved over them.

'Joe? Mr Dando ...?'

Pause. Listen. Nothing ... but then, from the darkness, came the sound of a racking, painful cough, a little to John's left. He crawled towards the sound, one hand combing the darkness in front of him ... until at last his fingers brushed against something soft and warm. As he ran his hand over it, he realised that he was caressing Joe Dando's face and bald head.

'Joe!' he cried. 'Joe!'

He placed his ear close to where he reckoned Joe's mouth was ... and yes, he could just about hear him breathing. A little laboured, perhaps, as though he had a heavy cold on his chest, but he *was* breathing.

Thank God!

Then John realised that he could actually make out the shape of Joe's head lying on the floor in front of him. How was that possible, when it was so incredibly dark down here? Perhaps his eyes were beginning to grow accustomed to the dark.

But no.

Looking up, he could see there was some kind of red glow in the distance. What on earth was it? Could it be possible that someone was coming to rescue them?

No, it wasn't that kind of light. This glow seemed to shudder, somehow, and it kept changing from red to orange and then back to red again.

And then John understood what it was, and why the pit felt so terribly hot.

The pit was on fire.

The emergency services finally arrived, and everything immediately became much more organised.

'But the trouble is,' one of the officers was heard to say, 'we can't go in until the fire has been put out. We're doing our best to sort that out now.'

They were, however, able to bring some of the colliers out from the pit, the ones who were caught between where the fire was at its worst, and the York Pit. Some of the ones who were still alive had been badly burnt in the explosion, and others were suffering from severe cuts and bruising, as well as broken bones, after having been hurled against the trucks and the pit walls.

But the majority were lying totally still on their stretchers, their bodies and faces concealed under blankets.

I can't look at them, thought Magwen, *but at the same time I can't look away from them either.* And the worst thing about them was that an occasional hand could be seen, dangling loose and limp and trailing heedlessly through the black dirt, having been shaken free as the stretchers were being carried.

The women waited in orderly rows by these terrible stretchers. One by one, their hands shaking with dread, the wives and mothers, the daughters and sisters, took hold of one corner of each blanket and lifted it slowly, all of them terrified of seeing the face of a loved one lying there. Some of them turned away with sighs of relief, others merely shook their heads – but all of them knew that they would have to do this over and over again until it became their turn to groan and weep.

This was when Edward Williams arrived back at Senghennydd, his diseased tooth extracted and his face, like everyone else's, filled with fear.

'Dad's come back, Mam,' said Magwen when she caught sight of Edward hurrying towards them.

Kate said nothing. She continued to stare towards the pit where the rescue crews were working flat out.

'Mam ...?'

Edward reached them and tried to place his arm around his wife's shoulders, but Kate shook him free impatiently.

'John?' asked Edward.

Kate shook her head. She hadn't once turned to look at

her husband. *What's the matter with her?* Magwen wondered. *Why is she behaving like this?* She'd expected her mother to have embraced her father, pleased to see him, just as Cerdiwen Dando had hugged Billy.

Edward turned away, looking totally lost. He noticed that a woman with long white hair, standing a little way off with Billy Dando and the rest of the Dando children, was staring at him. Who the heck was she? – and Edward realised with a jolt that it was Ceridwen Dando. But what had happened to her hair?

Then Ceridwen, too, turned her back to him.

'I ... I'm going to see if I can be of any help,' Edward said lamely.

Magwen watched her father walk away. She called after him, 'Dad!'

But Edward didn't hear her.

Even though he was surrounded by

hundreds of people, Magwen thought he was the loneliest man she'd ever seen.

How can such a small man weigh so much? thought John. He remembered how the Dando children, one day during the summer, had wheeled Joe up and down the street in a

wheelbarrow while he sang *Men of Harlech* at the top of his
voice.

But trying to move him now was like trying to move a
dram filled with coal. It's because of this heat, John decided.
He could see a little bit more by now, but that wasn't good
news as it meant that the fire was getting closer. And as it
burned, the fire sucked up what fresh air there was left inside

the mine. It wouldn't be long before none was left for John and Joe.

He struggled not to think of all the different gases – especially the nastiest one of them all, the after damp.

'Joe, come on, please try and help me a little,' whispered John. He managed to drag Joe a little bit further before having to rest and get his breath back. But as he turned, he felt something different under his foot. Something soft, but with something hard inside it.

The tommy-bag!

Oh, thank you, God, thank you, thank you! He fumbled for the bag and took out of it his drinking flask. The flask was filled with cold tea. Even though he felt as if he was almost dying of thirst himself, he decided that Joe needed it more than he did. He poured a little over Joe's lips ... then a little bit more ... and Joe coughed as the tea flowed down his throat. In the faint red glow of the fire, John saw his eyes open.

'Billy?' whispered Joe.

'No ... it's John. John Williams from next door,' John replied.

'Billy ...' Joe said again, before sinking back into unconsciousness.

John moistened his own lips before placing the flask safely inside his shirt. Perhaps the minute amount of tea had helped after all, or perhaps it was because Joe had opened his eyes and spoken, however briefly, but John managed to summon up a little more strength from somewhere – enough to drag Joe a little further up the tunnel and away from the fire, the fire that was getting closer and closer to the bend at the far end of the tunnel, like a determined red tide flowing towards them.

'It's impossible for anyone to survive a fire like this,' Edward heard one of the men say – and he came very close to punching him in the mouth. Didn't the idiot understand how important – and how fragile – hope was? He thanked God that none of the women had been close enough to have overheard this fool.

Then word came from the pit – they believed that they'd managed to put out the fire. The rescuers exchanged meaningful looks. It's our turn now, lads, said the looks. This was when their job began with a vengeance.

Kate's entire body was shivering, shivering like a jelly.

Magwen ran home to fetch overcoats and shawls for the two of them. As she went, she thought of what she'd heard someone say earlier – that the fire inside the pit had been raging like a furnace.

A furnace! Magwen thought of all the times she'd sat in front of the kitchen fire, staring into the flames and thinking how lovely the glowing red coals looked at the bottom of the grate.

Now, she couldn't think of them without picturing John lying in their midst.

The tea had all gone, the flask now empty.

What will I do now? John wondered. I can't drag poor old Joe much further: as it is I need to rest for several minutes, having only dragged him a foot or two.

And it was getting harder and harder to move him, as Joe seemed to get heavier with each passing minute. With each tug, John was panting as if he'd just been running a race – and breathing was becoming difficult, too. If anything, taking air into his body was causing him pain – it was burning him; he was sucking hot air into his lungs, and as he exhaled, John half expected to see smoke and flames shooting from his mouth, like that fire eater he'd watched when the circus visited Senghennydd two years previously. If that bloke was here now, he thought, he'd have one heck of a feast!

'Wouldn't he, Ned?' he said.

Somehow, Whatever Next Ned had arrived there from somewhere and was sitting beside him, looking down at him and Joe.

'What – he was really eating fire?' scoffed Ned. 'Stop talking rubbish, John Williams!'

'Yes, he was – I swear it,' insisted John. 'He had two long sticks, both of them on fire, and he fed them one by one into his mouth, and right down his throat.'

'Well!' exclaimed Ned. 'Whatever next?'

'Oh, Ned – d'you know what? I've missed you, mate,' said John, but when he turned to look, Ned had gone away.

'It's just you and me here now, Joe,' he said. 'Don't you worry, I won't let you disappear too.'

He held on tight to Joe Dando and closed his eyes. Five more minutes, he said to himself, just five more minutes ...

'No, hang about – this lad's still *alive*, boys!'

'What?'

'He is! I've just seen his lips move ...'

John could hear the voices, but he hadn't the strength to open his eyes. What was wrong with these people? Couldn't they see that he needed all his strength to hold on to Joe Dando? He wasn't about to let Joe slip away from him now, not after he'd gone to all that effort to drag him all this way.

'Good God! Don't tell me that he's dragged this man along with him?' he heard someone say.

Well, of course I have! thought John. That's what I've been trying to tell you – listen to me, can't you!

Then he heard another voice – a voice he recognised.

'Oh 'ngwas i! John! John! Are you with us?'

'Dad?'

John opened his eyes, only to shut them immediately because some idiot was shining a bright light into his face. But he'd caught a glimpse of his father's face gazing down at him.

And Edward Williams was crying.

Afterwards

Later, it was announced that 439 men and boys had been killed in the terrible Senghennydd disaster.

'You were incredibly lucky,' people kept telling John.

'Yes, I know I was,' he replied each time.

He quickly tired of hearing everyone tell him how lucky he'd been. He began to notice, too, how some people would say it in an odd way – almost grudgingly, as if they didn't like it that John had been one of the very few to have emerged alive from the Lancaster Pit.

'Don't be silly. Nobody thinks any such thing,' Kate chided him.

'Don't they? What about Billy next door, then?' said John.

Kate looked away. 'Give him time, John. He knows you did your very best to save his poor dad.'

'But I didn't manage it, though, did I?' said John. 'And I know a small part of Billy blames me for that.'

Joe Dando had in fact been alive when they pulled him out of the pit, along with John. But not for long – only long enough to open his eyes one more time. He'd begun to smile when he saw Cerdiwen's face looking down at him. But then the light had faded from his eyes, for ever.

'It wasn't all just down to luck, anyway,' Magwen said to John one evening.

'Wasn't it? What else was it then?' John whispered.

He could speak in nothing louder than a hoarse whisper for weeks following the disaster, for the hot, poisonous air he'd been breathing down the pit had damaged his throat. It took a long while for his voice to return to normal, and he understood that the hot air had burnt his larynx a little. And even though he finally recovered, for the rest of his life he kept tasting the gritty coal dust that had filled his mouth.

'I prayed for you, John,' Magwen said quietly.

'Did you?'

She nodded. 'Like I'd never prayed before in my life. Ever.'

'Oh ...' said John. 'Er ... thanks, Maggie.'

He hadn't quite known what to say. He thought that every woman and every girl – and every man, too, come to that, everyone who'd been waiting up on the surface – had been praying hard, too. Even though Magwen's little prayer may well have been answered, thought John, 439 other prayers had been ignored. Yes, I was lucky – very lucky.

But not as lucky as his father had been, many people marvelled. To have a raging toothache, on the very day the pit exploded!

'Would you credit it? I don't know how many people have come up to me, wanting to shake my hand in the hope that my good luck will rub off onto them,' said Edward Williams. 'As if I were a chimney sweep or something.'

But many other people shunned him; they either ignored him by turning their backs whenever they saw him, or crossed the street so they wouldn't have to look at him – including members of his choir and his chapel.

As though I carried *bad* luck with me everywhere, brooded Edward Williams. As if I was wearing it like I wear my cap or my coat.

And of course, this worried him greatly.

Ceridwen Dando called round one evening, not long after Joe's funeral had taken place. She wished to speak with Edward, but the first thing she said to him was, 'I really don't know what to say to you, Edward.'

She was finding it difficult to even look at him directly, Edward noticed. Her hair had remained as white as flour, and would do so for the rest of her days.

'The thing is, you were *supposed* to be there that day,' said Ceridwen.

'Oh, Ceri, I *know* that!' Edward sighed. 'I can barely think of anything else.'

Ceridwen nodded slowly. 'I don't suppose you can. And I know it was me who told you to go and see the dentist. But ... well, the thing is, a lot of people don't think that you should be going back there, to the pit.'

'What? Not go back to work?' said Edward.

'That's right. They believe that the pit hasn't finished with you yet.'

'What nonsense!' exclaimed Kate. 'I never in my life heard such rubbish. Ceridwen – *you* don't believe that, I hope?'

Ceridwen found it hard to look Kate in the eye. 'No ...' she said. 'My Joe wasn't supposed to be there, was he? Had he stayed in the York Pit, with Billy ... but the Lancaster Pit took him, instead of Edward.'

Edward Williams was quiet for a long while after Ceridwen had left. Finally, he said, 'That explains a lot of things, Kate.'

'It's all a load of nonsense!' was Kate's angry opinion.

'D'you think so?' Edward slowly raised his head and gazed

at her. '*Why him?* That's what everyone's thinking, love, every time they set eyes on me. *Why was he, of all people, allowed to live?* Kate, I'm not blind. I had my tooth removed that day, not my eyes. I can see it plainly on their faces – people who used to be our friends. I could even see it tonight, on Ceridwen's face.'

He paused, his eyes fixed on her face and full of sadness. Then he said, 'And I saw it on your face too, my love, when you were waiting outside the entrance to the pit that day.'

'Edward – no!'

'Oh, I don't blame you in the least, Kate, love. After all, you were almost insane with worry, fearing for our John ...'

'All right, Edward, that's enough!' said Kate firmly. 'I don't want to hear any more daft talk of that nature in this house again, d'you understand?'

Edward said no more. Indeed, he became much quieter and more morose as first the days, and then the weeks, went past. Yes, he did return to the pit, but something deep inside him had also died on that terrible October day.

Kate became very worried about him. She couldn't recall the last time she'd seen her husband smile, never mind heard him laugh out loud. He took to going out for hours, alone, wandering the mountain paths by himself until it was late at night.

'It's as if he's got a huge black cloud pressing down on him all the time,' Kate confided in Ceridwen one day.

Ceridwen said nothing in reply, but looked very uncomfortable when Kate referred to the cloud. One freezing February night, Edward Williams went out again. It began to snow not long afterwards, and Kate kept expecting to see him

return home, wet and shivering. But he didn't come. The hours dragged one by one as the snow fell heavier and heavier. Come morning, a gang of men went out to search for him. They found him on the mountainside, sitting there frozen solid with his hands inside his coat pockets, looking exactly as though he'd just fallen asleep.

In a way, John thought afterwards, that's precisely what his father had done. He'd sat down in the snow, closed his eyes ... and gone to sleep.

With the coming of spring, Kate, John and Magwen went back home. Back to their old home in north Wales.

'I've had enough of this place, John,' said Kate, who looked several years older than her age by then. 'I need to get away from here. I need to go home.'

As the train pulled out of the station, John found it impossible to drag his eyes away from the pit. He knew he'd be dreaming about it for the rest of his life.

'I'll never forget you, Senghennydd,' he said quietly. 'Ever. Neither will I ever forget you,' he said to the ghosts of all the men and young boys – all the butties who'd lost their lives that day. 'You'll all be with me for as long as I live.'

He started to turn away, but then realised there was someone standing by the trucks just outside the station, watching the train leave.

Billy Dando.

For a few seconds, John and Billy stared into one another's eyes. Then Billy half-raised his arm as though he were about to wave, but then, at the last minute, he seemed to change his mind.

He turned away from the train and began walking back.

To Senghennydd.

Epilogue

Fifty years on, watching the rain fall over the allotments, John Williams recalled his words of farewell to Senghennydd and its people.

Particularly to the dead.

'*I'll never forget you ... you'll all be with me for as long as I live.*'

No, he hadn't been able to forget, despite all his efforts.

He stood up and spat repeatedly. He could swear he could taste coal dust filling his mouth once again.

He wondered whether Magwen knew about this programme on television tonight. Did she even want to know? She was living in London now, had been for many years, having married a man who worked for one of the big banking companies. She and John hardly ever saw each other these days; a birthday card and a Christmas card, that was all the contact they had.

Truth be told (and John hadn't mentioned this to Betty),

the BBC had written to him asking if he'd be willing to take part in the Senghennydd programme, but he'd refused. Thanks ... but no, thank you. Now he asked himself, did I do the right thing?

Well, he reflected, it's too late now.

But he'd been right about one thing – he didn't require the help of some television programme to remember that one dark day. Hadn't he just done that very thing now, by himself?

And he'd needed no help from anyone to keep the promise he'd made almost fifty years ago to the people of Senghennydd – to the dead as well as to the living.

After all, some things are impossible to forget.